3 (a) Give the letter name of each of the notes marked ∗, including the sharp o
where necessary. The first answer is given.

C♯
....

(b) Complete this sentence: Each triplet (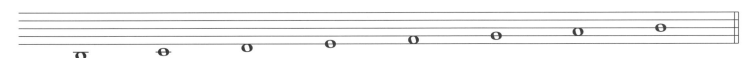) in bar 1 means three quavers (eighth notes) in the time

of ....

4 *Above* each note write a *higher* note to form the named *harmonic* interval, as shown in the [10]
first answer. The key is F major.

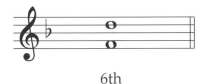   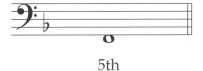   

6th   5th   3rd

4th   7th   8th/8ve

5 Add the correct clef and any necessary sharp or flat signs to make each of the scales [10]
named below. Do *not* use key signatures.

B♭ major

E minor

Which form of the minor scale have you used? ....

6 Name each key as shown by its key signature. The first answer is given.

...A... major   .... major   .... major

.... minor   .... major   .... minor

7 Rewrite the following in notes and rests of *twice* the value, beginning as shown.
Remember to group (beam) the notes correctly where necessary.

Devienne

4

8 Look at this melody by J. Besozzi and then answer the questions below.

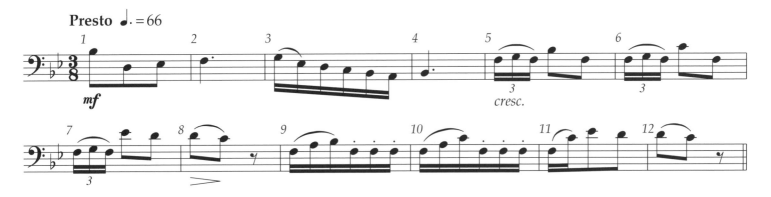

Write your answer to question (c) on the stave below.

(a) Give the meaning of each of these:

Presto ....

♩. = 66 ....

mf ....

cresc. (bar 5) ....

the dots above the notes (e.g. bar 9) ....

10

(b) (i) Give the letter name of the *highest* note in the melody. ....

10

(ii) Give the time name (e.g. crotchet or quarter note) of the rest in the last bar. ....

(iii) Answer TRUE or FALSE to this sentence:
This melody uses all the degrees of the scale of B♭ major. ....

(iv) Draw a circle around two notes next to each other that are a 5th apart.

(v) How many bars contain *only* semiquavers (16th notes)? ....

(c) Copy out the music from the first note of bar 9 to the end of the melody, exactly as it is written above. Don't forget the clef, key signature and all other details.
Write the music on the blank stave above question (a).
(Marks will be given for neatness and accuracy.)

10

Theory Paper Grade 2   2012   B

TOTAL MARKS
100

Duration 1½ hours

Candidates should answer ALL questions.
Write your answers on this paper – no others will be accepted.
Answers must be written clearly and neatly – otherwise marks may be lost.

1   Add the time signature to each of these five melodies.

10

2   Write a four-bar rhythm using the given opening.

10

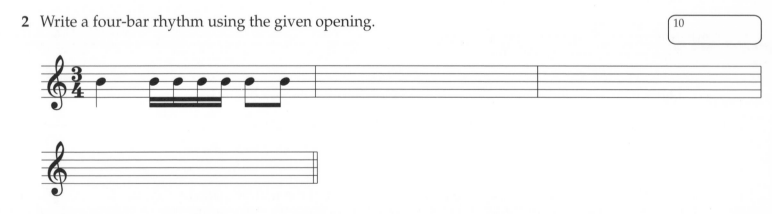

3 Add the correct clef and any necessary sharp or flat signs to make each of the scales named below. Do *not* use key signatures.

`10`

A major

E minor

Which form of the minor scale have you used? ....

4 (a) Give the letter name of each of the notes marked ∗, including the sharp or flat sign where necessary. The first answer is given.

`10`

C. G. Tag

Bb

(b) How many bars contain *only* crotchets (quarter notes)? ....

5 Write the time values in the correct order, from the *longest* to the *shortest*. The first answer is given.

`10`

6 Name the keys of these tonic triads.

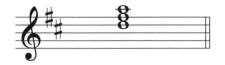 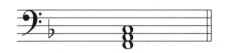 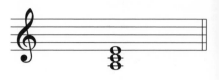

....

....

7 Rewrite this melody using the key signature of B♭ major. Leave out all unnecessary accidentals but remember to include any that are needed. The first two notes are given.

10

Beethoven

8 Look at this melody, adapted from a piece by Johann Strauss II, and then answer the questions below.

Write your answer to question (c) on the stave below.

(a) Give the meaning of each of these:

Andantino ....

p ....

mf (bar 4) ....

⟨ (bar 7) ....

∧ (e.g. bar 8) ....

[10]

(b) (i) This melody is in the key of C major. Give the number of a bar that contains all the notes of the tonic triad in this key.   Bar ....

(ii) Name the degree of the scale (e.g. 1st, 2nd) of the first note in the melody. Remember that the key is C major. ....

(iii) Give the letter name of the *lowest* note in the melody. ....

(iv) How many times does the rhythm ♩. ♪ occur? ....

(v) Underline one of the following words that best describes how you think bars 1–3 of this melody should be played:

     legato (smoothly) or *staccato* (detached)

[10]

(c) Copy out the music from the start of bar 5 to the end of the melody, exactly as it is written above. Don't forget the clef, dynamics and all other details. Write the music on the blank stave above question (a). (Marks will be given for neatness and accuracy.)

[10]

Theory Paper Grade 2   2012   C

DO NOT PHOTOCOPY
© MUSIC

TOTAL MARKS
100

Duration 1½ hours

Candidates should answer ALL questions.
Write your answers on this paper – no others will be accepted.
Answers must be written clearly and neatly – otherwise marks may be lost.

1   Add the missing bar-lines to these two melodies. The first bar-line is given in each.

10

2   Write a four-bar rhythm using the given opening.

10

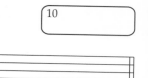

3   Add the correct rest(s) at the places marked ✱ in this melody to make each bar complete.

10

4   (a)   Name the degree of the scale (e.g. 2nd, 3rd) of each of the notes marked ✱, as shown
         in the first answer. The key is B♭ major.

10

   3rd
   ....

   (b)   Draw a circle around a note in this melody that is *not* in the key of B♭ major.

5 Give the number (e.g. 2nd, 3rd) of each of these melodic intervals, as shown in the first answer. The key is E♭ major. [10]

3rd
....

....

....

....

....

....

6 Add the correct clef to make each of these named notes, as shown in the first answer. [10]

C

E

middle C

B

D

G♯

A♭

F

E♭

G

F♯

7 Rewrite this melody in the bass clef, keeping the pitch the same. The first two beats are given. [10]

Anon.

11

8 Look at this melody by Mozart and then answer the questions below.

Write your answer to question (c) on the stave below.

(a) Give the meaning of each of these:

Andante ....

the **8** in $\frac{3}{8}$ ....

p ....

⌣ (bar 1) ....

the dots below the notes (bar 5) ....

[10]

(b) (i) Complete this sentence:
Bars 1 and 2 have the same notes and rhythm as bars .... and ....

(ii) Give the letter name of the last note in bar 5 (marked ✳). ....

(iii) This melody is in the key of A major. Draw a circle around three notes next to each other that form the tonic triad of this key.

(iv) Give the time name (e.g. minim or
half note) of the *longest* note in the melody. ....

(v) How many semiquavers (16th notes) are the tied notes in bars 6–7 worth in total? ....

[10]

(c) Copy out the music from the start of the melody to the end of bar 5, exactly as it is written above. Don't forget the clef, key signature, time signature, tempo marking, dynamic and all other details. Write the music on the blank stave above question (a). (Marks will be given for neatness and accuracy.)

[10]

Theory Paper Grade 2   2012   S

Duration 1½ hours

TOTAL MARKS
100

Candidates should answer ALL questions.
Write your answers on this paper – no others will be accepted.
Answers must be written clearly and neatly – otherwise marks may be lost.

1 (a) Name the degree of the scale (e.g. 2nd, 3rd) of each of the notes marked ∗, as shown
in the first answer. The key is D major.

10

3rd   ....

(b) Give the letter name of the *highest* note.   ....

2 Write a four-bar rhythm using the given opening.

10

3 Rewrite the following melody, grouping (beaming) the notes correctly.

10

4 Add the correct clef and key signature to each of these tonic triads.

E minor   Eb major   F major

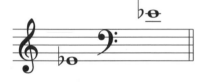   

A major   D minor

5 (a) Rewrite these treble clef notes in the bass clef, keeping the pitch the same.
    The first answer is given.

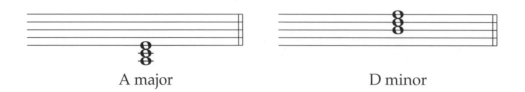

(b) In which major key are all these notes found? ....